Rebecca Meredith.

Equivalent fractions

Trace the rectangles. Join the dots as shown

Write down the fraction that is shaded and al

Example:

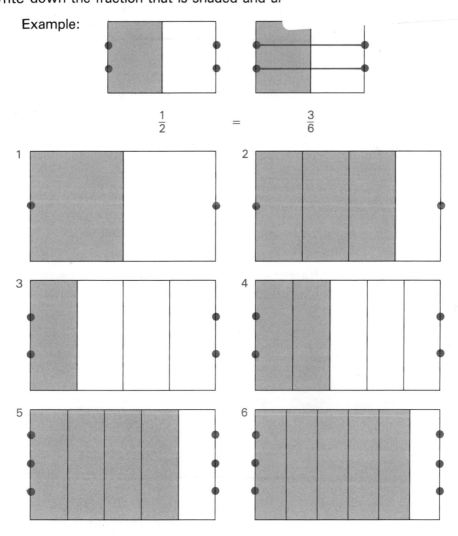

$$\frac{1}{2} \quad = \quad \frac{3}{6}$$

1

2

3

4

5

6

An equivalent fractions game

Step 1. Play this game with one or two friends.
Make 20 cards about 4 cm by 5 cm.
Write one of these fractions on each card:

$$\frac{1}{2}, \quad \frac{5}{10}, \quad \frac{3}{6}, \quad \frac{4}{8}, \quad \frac{1}{3}, \quad \frac{2}{6}, \quad \frac{3}{9}, \quad \frac{4}{12}, \quad \frac{2}{3}, \quad \frac{4}{6},$$

$$\frac{6}{9}, \quad \frac{8}{12}, \quad \frac{1}{4}, \quad \frac{2}{8}, \quad \frac{3}{12}, \quad \frac{4}{16}, \quad \frac{3}{4}, \quad \frac{6}{8}, \quad \frac{9}{12}, \quad \frac{12}{16}.$$

Step 2. Place the cards face downwards and mix them up thoroughly.
Arrange them in five rows with four cards in each row.

Step 3. The first player turns over two cards so that everyone can see them.
If they are equivalent fractions the player keeps them and has another turn.
If they are not equivalent fractions they are placed face downwards again and the next player has a turn.

Step 4. Play continues like this until all the cards have been taken.
The player with the most cards is the winner.

Make up some equivalent fractions of your own and play the game again.
Make sure you always have pairs of equivalent fractions in your pack of cards.

Estimating angles game

Work with one or more friends. You should each make a copy of this table.

Angle	My estimate	Actual measurement	Score
a			
b			
c			
d			
e			
f			
		Total	

First you should each write down your estimates for angle *a*.
Measure angle *a* with a protractor. If you were exactly right score 2 points; if you were within 10° of the answer score 1 point.
Estimate and measure the other angles. Add your scores to find the winner.

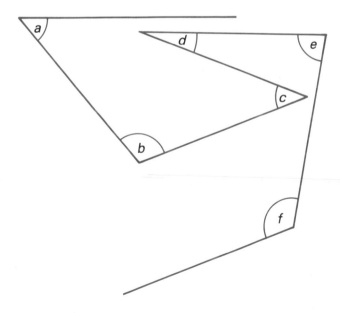

Area

You need some centimetre-squared paper.
Fiona drew round her hand so that she could find its area.

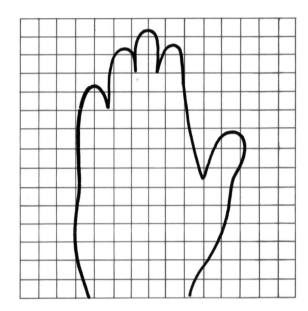

She wrote 1 in each complete square. The other squares she estimated to one place of decimals. She added her results to find the area of her hand.

1 (a) Estimate the area of your hand in square centimetres.
  (b) Use Fiona's method to find the area of your hand.

2 (a) Who do you think has: (i) the largest hand in your class?
                            (ii) the smallest hand in your class?
  (b) Estimate the area of their hands, then measure them.

3 Use the same method to find the area of your foot.

4 (a) Who do you think has: (i) the largest foot in your class?
                            (ii) the smallest foot in your class?
  (b) Estimate the areas of their feet, then measure them.

5 Some people have one foot slightly larger than the other. Do you?

Coordinates

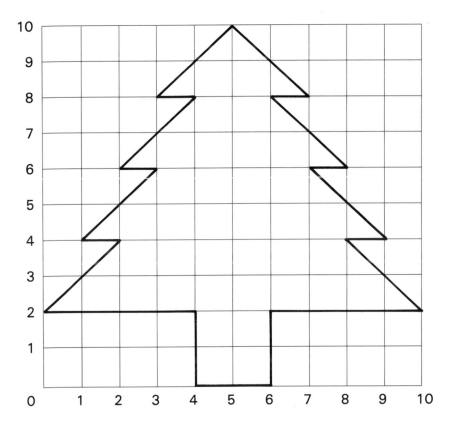

1 Write down, in order, the coordinates that are needed to give the picture of the tree. Start at (4,0).

2 (a) Draw a picture of your own on graph paper. Make sure you only use straight lines.
  (b) Write down the coordinates in order.
  (c) Swap your coordinates with those of a friend. Your friend should then draw your picture from your coordinates and you should draw your friend's picture.

Plotting coordinates

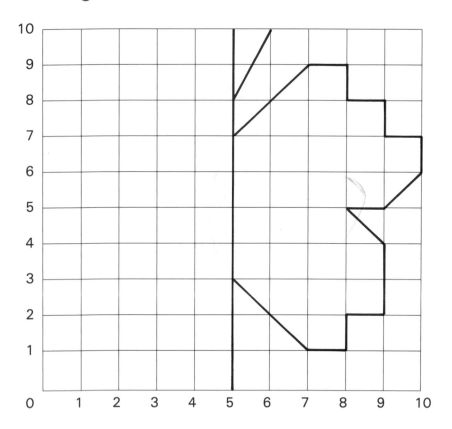

The line joining (5,10) to (5,0) represents a mirror.

1 Copy and complete the picture of the butterfly as it would be seen in the mirror.

2 The point (10,7) will be seen in the mirror at (0,7). We say (0,7) is the **mirror image** of (10,7).
Write down the mirror images of (7,9), (8,8), (10,6), (8,5), (9,2), (7,1), (5,3) and (5,7).

Circles from straight lines

Can you draw a circle using only a pencil and a ruler? The answer is 'No', but you **can** come very close to it!

Step 1. Mark a point on a piece of paper (X).

Step 2. Place one edge of the ruler so that it touches the point. (The dashed line shows the position of the ruler.)

Step 3. Draw a line along the other edge of the ruler (AB).

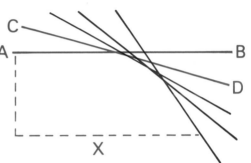

Step 4. Move the ruler round a little but keep the edge so that it touches X.

Step 5. Draw a line along the other edge (CD).

Step 6. Repeat the last two steps moving the ruler round a little each time.

You should see a 'curve' starting to appear after only a few lines have been drawn. The more lines you draw, the closer you will get to drawing a 'circle' with straight lines.

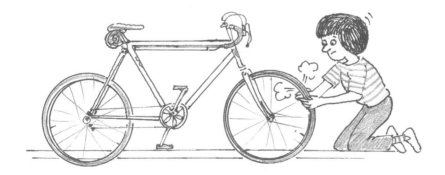

Curve stitching and drawing

The picture above was made by connecting the points as shown. You can make a curve stitching picture with a needle and coloured thread.

Make a picture by drawing. Follow these steps.

A Draw an angle.

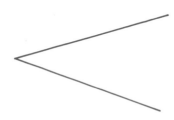

B Use a ruler and mark equally spaced dots as shown.
   Mark the same number of dots on each side of the angle.
   Number the dots as shown.

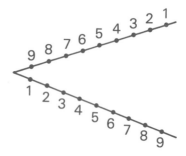

C Use a sharp pencil and ruler to connect the dots with the same number.

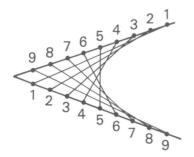

1 Design and draw your own picture. You may wish to work with more than one angle.

2 Make some pictures by curve stitching.

A subtraction game

Play this game with a friend. You need 30 counters. You can pick up 1, 2 or 3 counters when it is your turn.
The winner is the last person to pick up. Toss a coin to see who is to start.

Here is a game played by Jackie and Carl. Jackie won the toss so she started.

She picked up 3 counters. (27 left)

Carl picked up 2 counters. (25 left)

Jackie picked up 3 counters. (22 left)

Carl picked up 3 counters. (19 left)

Jackie picked up 1 counter. (18 left)

Carl picked up 3 counters. (15 left)

Jackie picked up 2 counters. (13 left)

Carl picked up 3 counters. (10 left)

Jackie picked up 3 counters. (7 left)

Carl picked up 1 counter. (6 left)   A

Jackie picked up 2 counters. (4 left)

Carl picked up 1 counter. (3 left)

Jackie picked up 3 counters and won.

1 Play the game several times with a friend.
   After tossing a coin to see who starts the first game, you should take it in turns to start.

2 How could Carl have won at the step marked A?

3 Can you work out how the first player can **always** win?

A decimal cross-number puzzle

This puzzle gives you practice in adding, subtracting and rounding decimals.

Copy the puzzle on to squared paper.

First solve the **Across** clues. Then solve the **Down** clues needed to complete the puzzle.

Solve the rest of the **Down** clues to help check your answers.

Don't write numbers in the boxes containing decimal points $\boxed{\bullet}$.

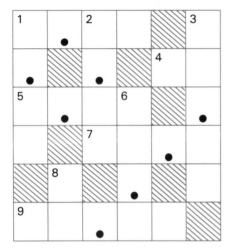

Across

1 Add 1.37 to 1.75.

4 Subtract 54.9 from 91.37.
   Round your answer to the nearest whole number.

5 Subtract 0.29 from 10.

7 Add 26.85 to 26.87.
   Round your answer to 1 place of decimals.

9 Add 3.9, 14.67 and 12.28.

Down

1 Subtract 0.04 from 4.

2 Add 0.36, 0.78 and 0.61.

3 Subtract 13.26 from 100.

6 Add 8.52 to 9.7 then subtract 4.4.
   Round your answer to 1 place of decimals.

8 Add 38.6, 20.49 and 30.51.
   Round your answer to the nearest whole number.

Decimal games

Any number can play.

Each player draws these boxes:

A   Using the digits 1, 2, 6, 7, 8 and 9 the players write one digit in each box to make the total as large as possible.
(There is only one possible largest total.)
The player who makes the largest total scores 1 point.

B   Draw the boxes again.
The problem this time is to make the smallest possible total.
The player who makes the smallest total scores 1 point.

C   Draw the boxes again but replace + by −.
Score 1 point for making the largest possible number.

D   Draw the boxes again. Using the − sign make the smallest possible answer. Score 1 point for it.

E   Using the + sign there are eight ways of making a total of 11.49. Score 1 point for each way you find.

How many points did you score?

Calculating weights

To find out how much one ball-point pen weighs, you can first weigh 10 identical pens to the nearest gram and then divide by 10.

Use this method to 'weigh' these objects.

1 A large nail

2 A pencil

> The more objects you weigh, the more accurate your answer will be.

You may use a calculator for the following questions.

3 Weigh 50 drawing pins. Find the weight of one drawing pin.

4 Weigh 50 matches. Find the weight of one match.

5 Find the weight of a sheet of paper.

6 Find some other small, light objects and calculate the weight of one of each sort.

Bang-Crash!

Play this game with some friends.

A To start with just play 'Bang'.
One person is leader and has to point to each player in turn.
As they are pointed at, the players say the numbers in order, but whenever
they reach a multiple of 6 the player whose turn it is must say "Bang".
So the first few numbers are as follows: 1, 2, 3, 4, 5, Bang, 7, 8, 9, 10,
11, Bang, 13 . . . and so on.
If a wrong response is given, that player drops out of the game.
The last player left is the winner.

B Now bring 'Crash' into it. The players must say "Crash" instead of each
multiple of 5.
So for 'Bang-Crash' the first few numbers are as follows:
1, 2, 3, 4, Crash, Bang, 7, 8, 9, Crash, 11, Bang, 13, 14, Crash, 16, 17,
Bang, 19 . . . and so on.
If a number is a multiple of 6 **and** 5 then say "Bang-Crash" or "Crash-
Bang".

C When you have played 'Bang-Crash' several times you can change the
rules and have other numbers instead of 6 and 5.

Age puzzle

Here is a method for finding the age of anyone aged 11 to 19.

An example is given for someone aged 15 years.

Tell the person to do these calculations.　　　　　　　　Example

Step 1. Multiply your age by 4.　　　　　　　　　　$15 \times 4 = 60$

Step 2. Add your age.　　　　　　　　　　　　　　$60 + 15 = 75$

Step 3. Multiply by 2.　　　　　　　　　　　　　$75 \times 2 = 150$

Step 4. Subtract 99.　　　　　　　　　　　　　　$150 - 99 = 51$

Step 5. Add the digits in the number you now have.　$5 + 1 = 6$

"Tell me the answer."

Step 6. Subtract 1 from the answer to find the units.　$6 - 1 = 5$

Step 7. Add 10.　　　　　　　　　　　　　　　　$5 + 10 = 15$

1 Check that this method works for all the other ages from 11 to 19.

2 Check that it does **not** work for anyone aged 10 or 20.

Find the object game

Play this game with some friends. You each need a metric ruler. Take it in turns to be the leader.

Step 1. In secret, the leader chooses an object and measures its greatest length to the nearest millimetre. For example, if a book is chosen measure its longest side; if a circular clock is chosen measure its diameter.
Leave the chosen object clear in view.

Step 2. When the group returns to the room the leader tells them the greatest length of the object they have to find.

Step 3. Everyone in the group writes down three objects they think might have been chosen by the leader. They must write them in order starting with what they consider to be the most likely choice.

Step 4. They each measure their three objects and write down their greatest lengths.

Scoring

Chosen object (or any other object that is exactly the given length)	Score 5
Any object within 2 mm of the chosen length	Score 4
Any object within 4 mm of the chosen length	Score 3
Any object within 6 mm of the chosen length	Score 2
Any object within 8 mm of the chosen length	Score 1
Any object more than 8 mm from the chosen length	Score 0

Play the game several times so that every member of the group has a turn at being leader. The person with the highest score is the winner.

How many ways will the shapes fit?

Trace the shapes below. Cut them out. Place them on a sheet of paper. Draw round them. Call the drawings the outline.

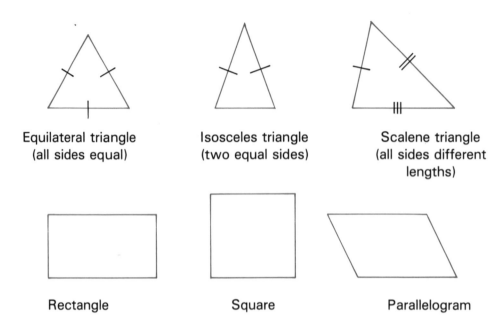

Equilateral triangle
(all sides equal)

Isosceles triangle
(two equal sides)

Scalene triangle
(all sides different
lengths)

Rectangle

Square

Parallelogram

1 Place the equilateral triangle on its outline in as many ways as you can. You can turn the triangle over. It helps to colour one side.
(You should find there are six different ways.)

2 Fit each of the other shapes on to their outlines in as many ways as you can.

3 Copy the table below. Enter your results from question 2 on to the table.

Shape	Equilateral triangle	Isosceles triangle	Scalene triangle	Rectangle	Square	Parallel-ogram
Number of ways it fits outline	6					

Quarter puzzles

1 This is exactly one quarter of a square:

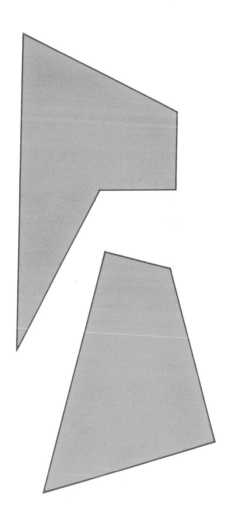

Trace it four times and cut out the shapes.
Fit them together to make a square.

2 Here are some more shapes that are all
exact quarters of a square.

Trace each shape and make four copies.
Fit them together to make squares.

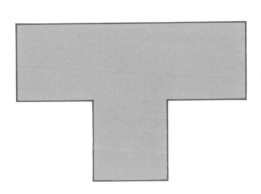

Buffon's problem

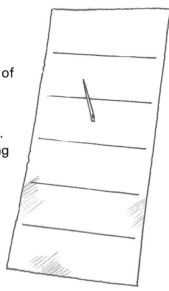

You need a needle.
Draw parallel lines to cover a large sheet of paper.
The distance between the lines must be the length of the needle.

1 (a) Without looking, drop the needle on to the paper. Record whether it crosses a line or not. (If it just touches a line count it as **not** crossing a line.)

   (b) Repeat (a) 99 more times.

2 Find the probability that the needle:

   (a) will cross a line $\left(\dfrac{\text{Number crossing}}{100}\right)$

   (b) will not cross a line $\left(\dfrac{\text{Number not crossing}}{100}\right)$

Check that your answers to (a) and (b) add up to 1.

3 **Buffon's Problem**
   A mathematician called Buffon worked out that the probability of the needle crossing a line was $\dfrac{2}{\pi}$.
   π stands for 3.14.

   (a) Use a calculator to find the value of $\dfrac{2}{\pi}$ to 2 places of decimals.

   (b) Find your answer to 2(a) to 2 places of decimals.
       Do you agree with Buffon?

Letter frequency

1 You need a book, magazine or newspaper.
   Start on any page you like and count the number of letters in each of the
   first 300 words. Record the results on a tally chart.
   5 is recorded like this: ➁⎜⎜⎜ .

   The total of the tallies is the frequency.
   For example, ➁⎜⎜⎜ ➁⎜⎜⎜ ⎜⎜⎜ is 13.

Number of letters in each word	Tally	Frequency
1		
2		
3		
4		
5		
6		
7		
8		
9		
10		
11		

2 What is the most frequent number of letters in a word?

3 (a) How many one-letter words did you find?
   (b) How many different one-letter words is it possible to have?

4 What is: (a) the most frequent three-letter word?
           (b) the second most frequent three-letter word?

5 Can you think how the answers to questions 3 and 4 could help in
   decoding messages that use a simple code?

A coordinate code

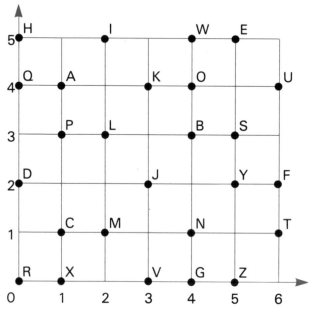

B is (4,3)
/ shows the end of a word.

1 Decode this message.
(6,1) (0,5) (5,5) / (1,3) (2,3) (1,4) (4,1) (5,3) / (1,4) (0,0) (5,5) /
(0,5) (2,5) (0,2) (0,2) (5,5) (4,1) / (4,3) (5,5) (0,5) (2,5) (4,1) (0,2) /
(6,1) (0,5) (5,5) / (1,1) (2,3) (4,4) (1,1) (3,4).

2 Work with a friend.
Code a message and give it to your friend to decode.
You decode your friend's message.

3 Make up a grid code of your own like the one above.
Form a secret group, each with the same grid code.
Send messages to each other and decode them.

Move the bird

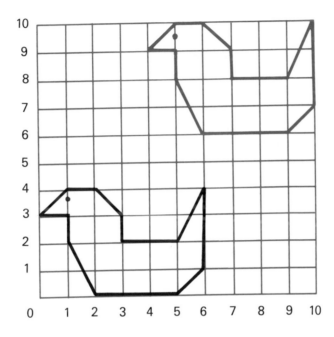

1 Are the black and the brown birds exactly the same size and shape?

2 Start with the point of the black bird's beak (0,3) and write down the coordinates of the rest of the bird going round in a clockwise direction so the second point will be (1,4).

3 Write down the coordinates of the corresponding points for the brown bird, starting at (4,9).

4 (a) Find a connection between the first number in the coordinates of the black and the brown birds.
  (b) Find a similar connection between the second number of the coordinates.

The results from question 4 are what you would expect if a shape is moved from one place to another but is not turned. A movement like this is called a **translation**.

Estimating a minute and making a graph

Sarah and a friend decided to see how well they could estimate a minute.
They got a stopwatch and Sarah told her friend when to start.
When she thought that a minute had passed, Sarah said "Stop!" The actual time was 51.8 seconds.
By how much did Sarah miss one minute?

1 Do this experiment in your class.
Each pupil should have a turn at estimating.
Keep a record of your class results like this:

One minute guesses			
Name	Time	Error in seconds	Error rounded to nearest second
Sarah	51.8	8.2	8

2 Make a bar graph of the errors rounded to the nearest second.

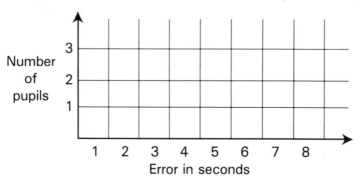

3 List some things that are shown on your graph.

4 If you have time, repeat the experiment, but this time estimate 30 seconds and compare your results.

Drip! Drip!

Let's find out how much water
Joanne wasted by leaving the tap
dripping all night.

1 Joanne left the tap dripping at 21:20 and
turned it off at 08:15 the next morning.
For how long was the tap dripping?

2 The dripping tap wasted 480 ml an hour.
At this rate, how many ml would be
wasted in:
(a) 1 minute? (b) 5 minutes? (c) 50 minutes? (d) 55 minutes?

3 (a) How many ml of water were wasted during the time Joanne left the
tap dripping?
(b) How much is that in litres?
(Remember: 1000 ml = 1*l*)

4 (a) Collect water from a dripping tap for 10 minutes.
(b) Use a measuring jug to find out the amount collected in millilitres.
(c) Calculate the amount of water you would expect to collect in an hour.

5 Make a list of all the ways you can think of to make sure water is not
wasted.

Casting out nines

Here is a way to check addition. You add the digits in each number until there is just one digit.

3847	$3 + 8 + 4 + 7 = 22$	$2 + 2 = 4$
2195	$2 + 1 + 9 + 5 = 17$	$1 + 7 = 8$
+4638	$4 + 6 + 3 + 8 = 21$	$2 + 1 = 3$
10 680	$1 + 0 + 6 + 8 + 0 = 15$	$1 + 5 = 6$

$4 + 8 + 3 = 15 \quad 1 + 5 = 6$

These two numbers **must** be the same or an error has been made.

Here is a simpler way which is based on the method above. It is called **'casting-out nines'**.

| 3847 |
| 2195 |
| +4638 |
| 10 680 |

Cross out any sets of digits, in the three numbers being added, if their sum is 9. Also cross out any 9s.
In this example the digits crossed out are 8 and 1, 7 and 2, 6 and 3, 4 and 5, and 9.
Add the digits left: $3 + 4 + 8 = 15 \quad 1 + 5 = 6$

The total reduces to 6 as before: $1 + 0 + 6 + 8 + 0 = 15 \quad 1 + 5 = 6$; or by 'casting-out nines': $1 + 0 + 6 + 8 + 0 = 6$.

1 Make up an addition of your own.
Check your addition by both of the methods shown.

2 Make up some more additions. Check them by using either method.

3
| 471 |
| − 186 |
| 285 |

You can also check subtraction by these methods.
Remember that $186 + 285$ must be 471.

So here is the check:

| 471 |
| − 186 |
| 285 |

$1 + 8 + 6 = 15 \qquad 1 + 5 = 6$
$2 + 8 + 5 = 15 \qquad 1 + 5 = 6$

$6 + 6 = 12 \qquad 1 + 2 = 3$

Check that 471 reduces to 3.

4 Try some subtractions and check them.

Percentages

Caroline and Martin asked different groups of pupils about their preferences.
26 out of 33 pupils preferred sausages to pork chops.

As a fraction this is $\frac{26}{33}$.

As a percentage it is $\frac{26}{33} \times 100$

which is 78.8% rounded to one place of decimals.

Use a calculator to find the following as percentages rounded to one place of decimals.

1 20 out of 32 pupils preferred games to music.

2 24 out of 26 girls preferred swimming to tennis.

3 31 out of 33 pupils preferred holidays to school days.

4 18 out of 31 girls preferred fiction to non-fiction books.

5 1 out of 29 pupils preferred school dinners to dinners at home.

6 15 out of 31 boys preferred BBC television to ITV.

7 23 out of 38 boys preferred dogs to cats.

8 7 out of 11 pupils preferred tea to coffee.

In the example at the top of the page, $\frac{7}{33}$ preferred pork chops to sausages. This is 21.2%.

The two percentages, 78.8% and 21.2% have a total of 100%.

9 Check questions 1 to 8 by calculating the other percentage in each case. Add each new percentage to the one originally found. The total should be 100% but accept 99.9% and 100.1% as correct answers because of rounding errors.

Choose the nearest

T M I C E R
1 2 3.4 5 6   metres

Each of the black letters has a value in metres. (Notice where the decimal point is written.) For example C is 0.4 metres, or 40 centimetres, E is 0.05 metres, or 5 centimetres.

1 Choose the black letter that gives the length **nearest** to each of these:
 (a) the length plus the width of your classroom;
 (b) the perimeter of a stamp;
 (c) the length of a sprint in the school sports;
 (d) the length of an eyelash;
 (e) the height of a room;
 (f) a cubit (elbow to fingertip).

If you have the answers right, the black letters will spell out a 'mathematical' word.

2 Now try this one:

A Q S E U R
9 8 7.6 5 4   kilometres

 (a) the distance walked in an hour;
 (b) the distance from Birmingham to Nottingham;
 (c) the height of the tallest tree in Great Britain;
 (d) the distance from Penzance to Glasgow;
 (e) the length of a garage;
 (f) the distance you could run in 2 to 3 minutes.

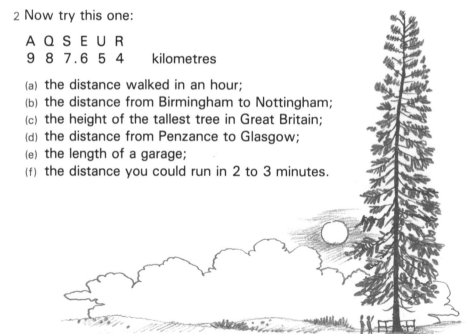

Perimeters

1 These shapes are not drawn accurately so do not measure any part of them.

Calculate their perimeters.

(a)

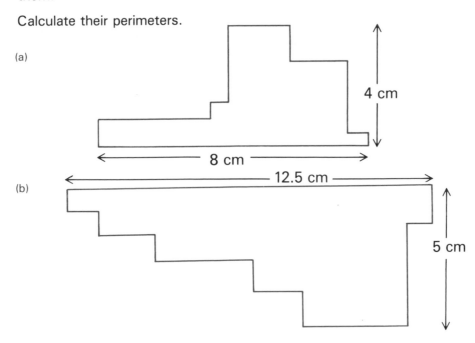

4 cm

8 cm

12.5 cm

(b)

5 cm

2 Measure the length and breadth of your school playing field.
Make a scale drawing of the field using a scale of 1 cm to 50 m.
(a) Calculate the perimeter of your plan in centimetres.
(b) Calculate the perimeter of the playing field in metres.

A measures puzzle

What would you have if you had 9 oranges in one hand and 8 oranges in the other hand?
Choose the closest answer for each question then write the letters down and they will spell out the answer to the riddle.

〰〰〰〰〰〰 This separates the words.

1	Capacity of a bath when full to the top.	N 30 *l*	V 400 *l*	S 1200 *l*
2	Amount of liquid you drink in a day.	E 2 *l*	T 10 *l*	A 30 *l*
3	Weight of a chicken.	P 0.2 kg	O 20 kg	R 2.0 kg
4	Volume of a brick.	S 2 m³	Y 700 cm³	U $\frac{1}{2}$ m³

〰〰〰〰〰〰〰〰〰〰〰〰〰〰〰〰〰〰〰〰〰〰

5	Capacity of a thimble.	L 3 ml	B 40 ml	A 0.1 ml
6	Weight of a letter.	A 35 g	D 3.5 g	C 350 g
7	Volume of a small room.	C 80 m³	L 14 m³	R 32 m³
8	Capacity of a bucket.	H 7 *l*	G 28 *l*	I 85 *l*
9	Volume of wood in a tree.	R 80 m³	V 200 m³	E 5.5 m³

〰〰〰〰〰〰〰〰〰〰〰〰〰〰〰〰〰〰〰〰〰〰

10	Weight of a large man.	L 18.8 kg	H 88 kg	A 192 kg
11	Capacity of a teacup.	A 200 ml	G 2000 ml	J 20 ml
12	Volume of a house.	P 1200 m³	K 2000 m³	N 200 m³
13	Weight of a teaspoon.	D 20 g	C 100 g	F 350 g
14	Capacity of a very large spoon.	E 170 ml	R 80 ml	S 15 ml

A target number game

This is a game for two or more players.
Each player needs a calculator, paper and a pencil.
The object is to reach your target number and never to go above 999 999.

Step 1. Each player chooses a 5-digit number and writes it on the paper
without letting the other players see it.
These numbers are the players' target numbers.

Step 2. The players then choose a 1-digit starting number in turn, each
choosing a different number.

Step 3. The last player to choose then starts the game by announcing a 1-,
2- or 3-digit number and any one of the operations addition,
subtraction, multiplication or division.

Step 4. All the players then carry out the operation on their starting
numbers.

Step 5. The other players choose a number and an operation in turn and all
the players carry that out on their numbers.

Any player getting over 999 999 drops out of the game.

The winner is the first player to reach his or her target number or to force all
the other players to get over 999 999.
Each player must allow the others to see the number on his or her calculator.

Gemma, Gary, Penny and Trevor played the game.
Here are Gemma's calculations.
Her target number is 38 719 and her starting number is 6.

Gemma says "Multiply by 146." Gemma's calculator shows 876.
Gary says "Add on 500." Gemma's calculator shows 1376.
Penny says "Multiply by 7." Gemma's calculator shows 9632.
Trevor says "Multiply by 4." Gemma's calculator shows 38 528.
Gemma says "Add 191." Gemma's calculator shows 38 719.
So Gemma wins.

Play the game with some friends.

Tangrams

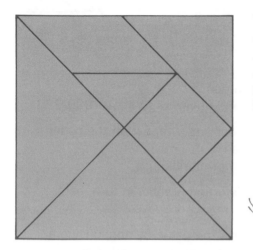

Tangrams are Chinese puzzles invented nearly 4000 years ago.
A square is divided into seven pieces as shown, the pieces can then be re-arranged to make pictures and interesting shapes.

Trace the square and cut out the shapes.

1 Make some pictures with the shapes. Here is an example to help you start.

Aladdin's lamp.

2 Use the two small triangles to make:
(a) a square; (b) another triangle; (c) a parallelogram.
(A parallelogram is a four-sided shape with each pair of opposite sides parallel.)

3 Use any three pieces you like to make a rectangle.

4 (a) Use two pieces to make a trapezium.
   (A trapezium is a four-sided shape with one pair of opposite sides parallel.)

   (b) Now make a trapezium using three pieces.

5 Make a triangle with: (a) 3 pieces; (b) 4 pieces.

6

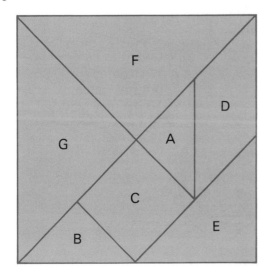

Write these letters on your shapes. We will use the small triangle A as the unit of area.
A = **B** as **A** and **B** have the same area.

How many times can triangle **a** be fitted on to:
(a) square **C**?   (b) triangle **E**?   (c) triangle **G**?   (d) parallelogram **D**?

7 The area of triangle **A** can be expressed as a fraction of the area of parallelogram **D**. We can write it as $\frac{A}{D}$.

This is $\frac{1}{2}$ since **D** is the same as **A** multiplied by 2.

Write these fractions in lowest terms.

(a) $\frac{A}{G}$ (b) $\frac{A}{F}$ (c) $\frac{E}{F}$ (d) $\frac{D}{G}$ (e) $\frac{C}{G}$

Watch it!

Give all your answers as 24-hour clock times.

1 Sarah and Justin agreed to meet at 19:00.

I'll put my watch 10 minutes fast. So I'll be early if I get there when my watch says 19:00.

I want to be 10 minutes early. So I'll put my watch 10 minutes slow.

(a) Who was right?

(b) How long would the first one to arrive have to wait for the other one?

2 David's watch was 5 minutes fast.
Pam's watch was 8 minutes slow.

(a) What time did Pam's watch show when David's watch showed 20:00?

(b) What time did David's watch show when Pam's watch showed 22:50?

3 Melanie arrived at work at 09:00. She went to lunch at 13:00 and returned at 13:50. She had a tea break between 15:04 and 15:15. She finished work at 17:30. It took her 20 minutes to get home, 5 minutes longer than it took her to get to work. Her watch was 11 minutes slow.

(a) What time did her watch say when she left for work in the morning?

(b) Her watch said 07:30 when she got up. How long did she have before she had to leave for work?

(c) What time did she arrive home?

(d) How long (in hours and minutes) did she work for?